MW00610612

MacArthur Competence Assessment Tool For Treatment (MacCAT-T)

Thomas Grisso and Paul S. Appelbaum

University of Massachusetts Medical School

Developed with support from the
John D. and Catherine T. MacArthur Foundation
Research Network on Mental Health and the Law

Professional Resource Press
Sarasota, FL

Published by Professional Resource Press
(An imprint of Professional Resource Exchange, Inc.)
Post Office Box 15560
Sarasota, FL 34277-1560

The copy editor for this book was Judith Warinner, the managing editor was Debra Fink, and the cover and text were designed by Laurie Girsch.

Library of Congress Cataloging-in-Publication Data

Grisso, Thomas.
    MacArthur competence assessment tool for treatment (MacCAT-T) / Thomas
Grisso, Paul S. Appelbaum.
      p.   cm.
    "Developed with support from the John D. and Catherine T. MacArthur
Foundation Research Network on Mental Health and the Law."
    Includes bibliographical references (p.   ).
    ISBN 1-56887-041-8 (alk. paper)
    1. Patient participation. 2. Informed consent (Medical law)
I. Appelbaum, Paul S. II. Title.
R727.42.G75   1998 Suppl.
610.69'6--dc21
          98-19161
          CIP

TABLE
OF CONTENTS

PREFACE

The MacArthur Competence Assessment Tool for Treatment (MacCAT-T) is a structured interview schedule for assessing decisionmaking abilities relevant for judgments about patients' competence to consent to treatment. It is the final product of the MacArthur Civil Competence Project, a program of research on informed consent and patients' decisionmaking capacities conducted from 1989 to 1997. This program of research was made possible by the John D. and Catherine T. MacArthur Foundation through its support for the MacArthur Research Network on Mental Health and the Law, of which we were core members. We were given primary responsibility by the Network to develop and manage the research that led to this instrument, but its conceptualization and final form were clearly a group product. We wish to thank the other members of the Network who made enormous contributions to the MacCAT-T's development throughout the research effort. They are Shirley Abrahamson, Richard Bonnie, Pamela Hyde, John Monahan (Chair), Stephen Morse, Ed Mulvey, Loren Roth, Paul Slovic, Henry Steadman, and David Wexler.

Development of the MacCAT-T followed our experience in constructing three research measures that we used to assess patients' decisionmaking capacities in informed consent to treatment. Those Civil Competence Research Instruments are described elsewhere (Grisso & Appelbaum, 1995; Grisso et al., 1995). They were very useful as objective measures of relevant decisionmaking abilities with which we tested hypotheses about the relation of decisionmaking deficits to medical and mental disorders. As tools for use by clinicians, however, they required too much time and effort to meet the demands of everyday clinical practice. The MacCAT-T reflects our decision to merge the three measures into one clinically portable tool, retaining as much of the format of the research instruments as possible but providing simpler administration and response rating criteria.

The MacCAT-T manual and a sample of the MacCAT-T Record Form were originally printed in the Appendix of our book, published by Oxford University Press, entitled *Assessing Competence to Consent to Treatment: A Guide for Physicians and Other Health Professionals* (Grisso & Appelbaum, 1998). While it was important to include the contents of the manual in the book, it was unwieldy for clinicians to use it in that form in everyday practice. Moreover, the book's copy of the record form, intended merely to describe the form, was printed in a reduced size that was not feasible for actual use by clinicians for recording patients' responses.

To remedy this situation, Professional Resource Press obtained permission from Oxford University Press to publish the MacCAT-T manual separately in its present form, which is much more suitable for use as reference material in residency and continuing education programs, and more feasible for clinical use at bedside or as a desktop reference. The MacCAT-T Record Forms have now been produced in a size that is appropriate for easy recording of MacCAT-T interview information, and in a trifold layout that allows all information to be on a single document rather than on several pages that might become separated. Packages of the record form can be purchased from Professional Resource Press.

This manual describes the MacCAT-T interview procedure, but actually seeing a sample interview being performed conveys the process and its nuances much more effectively than any written description can accomplish. Thus we have produced a videotape that shows a clinician performing the MacCAT-T interview with a patient with schizophrenia, accompanied by our own narrative and comments for each stage of the interview. The videotape will be especially valuable in residency education and continuing education workshops as a teaching tool and a medium for group discussion regarding the clinical process of assessing competence to consent to treatment. This videotape is also available from Professional Resource Press.

Finally, we caution readers that the MacCAT-T manual itself does not provide all of the information that clinicians will need in order to perform competency assessments regarding patients' abilities to make informed treatment decisions. Clinicians must also know the meaning of informed consent, the relation of competence to informed consent, the role of clinical diagnostic information in interpreting the MacCAT-T, and the legal and clinical framework in which judgments about patients' competence must be made. The MacCAT-T assesses certain specific abilities that are important for competence, but one must also grasp the conceptual and clinical context within which to interpret these results. All of these matters are reviewed in our book, *Assessing Competence to Consent to Treatment*. Therefore, we consider the book and this manual to be a "set" for purposes of clinicians' performance of competence assessments.

Thomas Grisso
Paul S. Appelbaum

Worcester, MA
July, 1998

MacArthur Competence Assessment Tool For Treatment (MacCAT-T)

INTRODUCTION

The MacArthur Competence Assessment Tool for Treatment (MacCAT-T) offers physicians and other health professionals practical guidance in their assessments of patients' decisionmaking capacities in the context of informed consent to treatment. The MacCAT-T is an interview guide that helps clinicians to obtain from patients information that is especially relevant for judgments about patients' competence to consent to or refuse treatment.

The MacCAT-T interview was developed to combine the process of preparing patients to make informed treatment decisions and the assessment of their capacities to decide. Information about the patient's own disorder, the treatment options, and their benefits and risks are entered on the MacCAT-T Record Form prior to the clinician's interview with the patient. The MacCAT-T then guides the clinician through a process of informing the patient of those factors that should be considered when providing informed consent. Questions prompted by the MacCAT-T interview procedure elicit answers in a manner that reveals the patients' degree of ability in four areas: *Understanding, Appreciation, Reasoning,* and *Expressing a Choice.* Patients' responses are evaluated using the instrument's criteria for rating their adequacy in each of the four areas of decisionmaking capacity.

The four areas of ability assessed by the MacCAT-T were determined through comprehensive reviews of legal definitions of competence to consent to treatment (Appelbaum & Grisso, 1988, 1995; Appelbaum & Roth, 1981, 1982; Berg, Appelbaum, & Grisso, 1996). Complete definitions of these ability concepts and case examples to illlustrate them are provided in *Assessing Competence to Consent to Treatment* (Grisso & Appelbaum, 1998). In brief, they are defined as follows:

- *understanding* of treatment-related information, focusing on categories of information that must be disclosed as required by the law of informed consent.
- *appreciation* of the significance of the information for the patient's situation, focusing on the nature of the disorder and the possibility that treatment could be beneficial.

1

- *reasoning* in the process of deciding upon treatment, focusing on the ability to compare alternatives in light of their consequences, including the ability to draw inferences about the impact of the alternatives on the patient's *everyday* life.
- *expressing a choice* about treatment.

The MacCAT-T rating criteria provide a way for the clinician to express opinions concerning the adequacy or inadequacy of each of the patient's responses. A summary of the patient's ratings for questions within a particular type of ability provides an indication of the adequacy or degree of deficits in the patient's abilities to deal with information and decisions about his or her own disorder and treatment. However, the MacCAT-T does not provide "cut-off scores" that represent "competence" or "incompetence" on the four abilities. This is because the MacCAT-T was designed to be consistent with a basic maxim in the legal definition of competence: No particular level of ability is always associated with competence or incompetence across all patients, all disorders, and all medical situations. (See Chapter 2 in Grisso & Appelbaum, 1998, for an explanation of this maxim as well as others that are important for understanding legal competencies.)

Moreover, the MacCAT-T does not provide an overall "MacCAT-T total score." It provides ratings on each of the four areas of decisional ability described earlier, but does not sum these scores. This is related to a basic concept of competence: In some cases, a serious deficit in ability in any one of the four areas may translate to a clinical or judicial opinion about incompetence, even if the patient's capacities in the other three areas are quite adequate.

When clinicians use the MacCAT-T in assessments of patients' capacities to make treatment decisions, it is essential that the results be integrated with other clinical and background data, as well as a consideration of the context in which the interview procedure was employed. It is a misuse of the MacCAT-T to make judgments about patients' competence to consent to treatment simply on the basis of their MacCAT-T scores. The complete process for assessing patients' treatment decisionmaking capacities is described in the book noted previously, with which clinicians who use the MacCAT-T should be familiar.

Administration of the MacCAT-T involves three steps: *Preparation*, in which the clinician obtains and organizes information (on the MacCAT-T Record Form) about the patient and the treatment options in order to construct the disclosure for the interview; the *Interview* itself; and *Rating* of the patient's performance on interview inquiry questions. The manual is outlined according to these three headings. A videotape demonstrating the administration of the MacCAT-T in a doctor-patient interview can be obtained from Professional Resource Press.

I. Preparation

Prior to meeting with the patient, the clinician prepares the information that will be disclosed to the patient. When the clinician is the patient's doctor, the clinician will already be well informed about the patient's disorder and treatment needs. If the clinician who is performing the assessment is not the treating clinician, the information necessary for preparing the disclosure and assessment process must be obtained from the treating clinician and/or the patient's chart.

1. *Diagnosis of Disorder.* Determine the patient's diagnosis, and write its name in Disclosure space #1 on page 1 of the Record Form.

2. *Features of Disorder.* Select three features of the disorder that are most important for the patient to understand in order to make an informed decision about treatments. Write descriptions of these features in Disclosure spaces #2-4 on page 1 of the Record Form. "Features" of a disorder that are appropriate to disclose will vary considerably across disorders and circumstances, and will depend in part on whether the symptoms of the disorder are primarily biological or psychosocial in nature. Possibilities include descriptions of critical biological mechanisms, causes, signs, and symptoms.

3. *Course of Disorder.* Determine the probable course of the disorder if no treatment were to be provided. Write a description of the untreated consequences of the disorder in Disclosure space #5 on page 1 of the Record Form.

4. *Recommended Treatment.* Determine the treatment that, in the judgment of the treating clinician, is in the best medical interest of the patient, and write it in Disclosure space #1 on page 2 of the Record Form.

5. ***Features of Recommended Treatment.*** Select two or three features of the treatment that are important for the patient to understand in order to make an informed decision, and write the descriptions in Disclosure spaces #2-4 on page 2 of the Record Form. Features of a treatment disclosed at this point should not include benefits or risks. The focus here is on the treatment process - for example, what preparation is required, the medical procedure itself, follow-up procedures, and duration of treatment.

6. ***Benefits/Risks of Recommended Treatment.*** Determine two of the most important expected *benefits* of the treatment, as well as the best possible estimate of their likelihood to occur. Write the descriptions, including their likelihood, in the Disclosure spaces #1-2 on page 3 of the Record Form. Then determine the most important expected *risks, discomforts, and/or side-effects* of the treatment, as well as the best possible estimate of their likelihood to occur. Write the descriptions, including their likelihood, in Disclosure spaces #3-4 on page 3 of the Record Form.

7. ***Alternative Treatments.*** (OPTIONAL) Repeat Steps 4 to 6 for any alternative treatments to be disclosed to the patient, recording the information on the Alternative Treatments (AT) Form.

NOTE: Step 7 is not essential for performing an assessment of the patient's decisionmaking capacities; the patient's performance related to the treatment chosen in Step 4 may be representative of the patient's functioning in making treatment decisions in general. Step 7 may be useful, however, in cases in which documentation of patients' understanding of all options is desirable - for example, in complex cases that may require judicial (court) review.

II. INTERVIEW

PROCEDURE

The MacCAT-T interview procedure combines the disclosure of informed consent information with assessment of patients' abilities to comprehend the information and make decisions about their treatment. The interview should proceed in the sequence described on the next page. Some flexibility is allowable, however, to meet the needs of specific patients, as long as all parts of the interview procedure are completed by the end of the interview.

STYLE

Throughout the interview, it is important for clinicians to adapt their disclosure and questioning (vocabulary, sentence lengths, pace) to the verbal abilities, level of intelligence, and emotional needs of the patient.

RECORDING

The patient's responses to inquiries throughout the interview should be recorded in the spaces on the Record Form marked "Response." Ratings of the patient's Understanding, Appreciation, Reasoning, and Choice will be made later on the basis of the clinician's notes in these spaces. The Record Form also provides brief prompts to the clinician that are related to the more lengthy description of the interview on the following pages.

Introduction

Describe to the patient the purpose of the present interview, framing it as a consultation and discussion. Indicate that you will describe what you believe is the patient's medical problem and possible courses of treatment, and that you will want to discuss the patient's understanding of the information. Encourage the patient to ask questions as the interview proceeds.

1. ***Disclose.*** Using the information prepared in the Disclosure spaces, describe the disorder and its elements. Ask if there are any questions; if there are, answer them.

2. ***Inquire.*** Tell the patient that you wish to make sure that he or she has understood what you have described. Ask the patient to describe to you his or her understanding of the information: what the disorder is called, what is wrong, what will happen if it is not treated, and so forth. Write down responses in the appropriate space on page 1 of the Record Form.

3. ***Probe.*** When a patient's description omits information for any of the important elements, use a prompt to make inquiry about what he or she recalls and understands concerning that portion of the disclosure. For example, if the patient does not describe the probable untreated course of the disorder, say "Tell me what will happen if we don't treat the problem - if we just let it go." Write responses on the Record Form.

4. ***Re-Disclose and Re-Inquire.*** For any of the important elements that the patient (a) has not described after Inquire and Probe or (b) has described incorrectly, explain those elements to the patient again, and again inquire concerning the patient's comprehension of the information. Write responses on the Record Form.

NOTE: During the inquiry, some patients might respond, not by describing the disorder, but by describing their beliefs or disbeliefs regarding the information that was disclosed as it pertains to their own situation (e.g., "Why are you saying I have angina - I'm sure it's just heartburn"). In such cases, the clinician can move ahead to explore the patient's appreciation (described in the next section). However, it is very important to return eventually to the Understanding-Disorder discussion, in order to assure that the patient does comprehend the disclosure, despite perhaps believing that it is not applicable to his or her own situation. Patients' *beliefs*, in contrast to their *understanding* of what they have been told, are the focus of the next section of the interview.

Appreciation-Disorder

The purpose of this section is to determine (a) whether the patient acknowledges that he or she has the disorder and its symptoms as disclosed previously and, if not, (b) the patient's alternative explanations and reasons for disbelieving that the previous disclosure applies to his or her own situation. To obtain this information, the clinician may use whatever approach to questioning is comfortable. The following are general guidelines:

1.   ***Inquire.*** For example, "Now that is what your doctors (or "we" if appropriate) think is the problem in your case. If you have any reason to doubt that, I'd like you to tell me so. What do you think?" Write responses on page 2 of the Record Form.

2.   ***Probe.*** If a patient expresses disagreement with the diagnosis or features of the disorder as applied to himself or herself, the clinician must determine through discussion the basis for the disbelief. The basis may be challenged by the clinician in order to determine whether it is easily modified or rigidly held. Write responses on the Record Form.

When exploring the patient's belief, pay particular attention to the fact that:

- Both acknowledgment and nonacknowledgment of the disorder may occur on the basis of illogical, bizarre, or delusional ideas.
- Patients' nonacknowledgment that the description of the disorder applies to themselves may be based on experiences that logically lead to that conclusion (e.g., patients have received different diagnoses for the same symptoms during past medical consultations).
- Nonacknowledgment may be based on beliefs that are commonly held in certain religious or cultural groups with which the patient is associated, and in that social context the belief may not be illogical, bizarre, or delusional.

Understanding-Treatment

This section proceeds in the same manner as described previously for Understanding-Disorder: Disclose, Inquire, and if necessary, Probe, Re-Disclose, and Re-Inquire. Write responses on page 2 of the Record Form.

Understanding-Benefits/Risks

This section proceeds in the same manner as described previously for Understanding-Disorder: Disclose, Inquire, and if necessary, Probe, Re-Disclose, and Re-Inquire. Write responses on page 3 of the Record Form.

Appreciation-Treatment

The purpose of this section is to determine (a) whether the patient acknowledges that the proposed treatment *might* be of some benefit and, if not, (b) the patient's explanations and reasons for disbelieving that treatment might have some benefit in his or her own situation.

It is *not* the purpose of this procedure to determine whether the patient is accepting the treatment. It also is not of importance whether the patient speaks favorably about it. The purpose is to determine whether the patient is unwilling even to consider (acknowledge the possibility of) the treatment because of confused, delusional, or affective states related to mental disorder.

To obtain this information, the clinician may use whatever approach to questioning is comfortable. However, at this point, phrasing of the questions should carefully avoid focusing on whether the patient is actually accepting or rejecting the treatment. The following are general guidelines for the questioning:

1. ***Inquire.*** "In a moment I am going to tell you a bit more about your choices for treatment. But first I want to see how you feel about the one we've just discussed. You might or might not decide that this is the treatment you actually want - we'll talk about that later. But do you think it's possible that this treatment might be of some benefit to you?"

2. ***Probe.*** Whether the patient believes or does not believe that the treatment could be of some benefit, determine through discussion the basis for the belief. Record the patient's responses on page 4 of the Record Form. The basis may be challenged by the clinician, in order to determine whether it is easily modified or rigidly held. For example: "So you feel that it is/isn't possible for that treatment to be of some help for your condition. Can you explain that to me? What makes it seem that the treatment would/wouldn't be of possible benefit to you?"

When exploring the patient's beliefs, pay particular attention to the fact that:

- Both acknowledgment and nonacknowledgment of the potential value of a treatment may occur on the basis of illogical, bizarre, or delusional ideas.
- Nonacknowledgment of the potential value of a treatment may be based on past experience that logically leads to the presumption that the treatment would be of little benefit (e.g., the patient received this treatment in the past with no significant benefit).
- Nonacknowledgment may be based on beliefs that are commonly held in certain religious or cultural groups with which the patient is associated, and in that context may not be illogical, bizarre, or delusional.

Alternative Treatments

As noted earlier, this step is not essential for performing an assessment of the patient's decision capacities; the patient's performance when addressing questions concerning the recommended treatment on which the disclosure focuses may be used in many instances as representative of the patient's functioning in treatment decision situations in general. This step may be useful, however, in cases in which documentation of a patient's understanding of all options is desirable, for example, in complex cases that may require judicial review.

If alternative treatments are described to the patient, repeat the procedures for Understanding-Treatment and Understanding-Benefits/Risks for each of the alternatives. Responses should be recorded in the spaces provided on additional Record Form pages (see Alternative Treatment [AT] Form) in the same manner as with the Recommended Treatment.

First Choice and Reasoning

The First Choice and Reasoning portion of the MacCAT-T interview involves a discussion between clinician and patient that explores the patient's treatment choice and how the patient is arriving at this choice. The following sequence of questions is recommended:

1. *Choice.* "Now let's review the choices that you have. First . . .; second . . .; and so on (name each treatment option reviewed earlier in the disclosure, including no-treatment option). Which of these seems best for you? Which do you think you are most likely to want?" Record the patient's response in the space marked

"Choice" on page 4 of the Record Form. If the patient states more than one choice among which he or she is reluctant to choose, write down each of them.

2.   *Inquire.* "You think that (state patient's choice) might be best. Tell me what it is that makes that seem better than the others." Record patient's response in the space provided for Reasoning at the bottom of page 4 of the Record Form.

3.   *Probe.* Repeat the reasoning back to the patient in your own words. Then engage in at least a brief discussion of the patient's explanation, asking any questions that will help you to understand and describe the patient's reasoning. Write responses as appropriate on the Record Form.

Generate Consequences

The purpose of this discussion is to determine whether the patient is able to translate medical circumstances of the disorder and treatment (e.g., symptoms, benefits, and risks of treatment) into their practical, everyday consequences (e.g., effect on work or recreation, effect on interpersonal relations). The following process is recommended:

Inquire-1.   "I told you about some of the possible benefits and risks or discomforts of (name the patient's preferred treatment). What are some ways that these might influence your everyday activities at home or at work?" Record response in Consequence-1 on page 5 of the Record Form.

Inquire-2.   "Now let's consider (name any other treatment or the no-treatment option). What are some ways that the outcome of that option might influence your everyday activities at home or at work?" Record response in Consequence-2 on page 5 of the Record Form.

Final Choice

1.   *Inquire.* "When we started this discussion, you favored (insert 'First Choice' from earlier inquiry, or note that the patient seemed to be having difficulty deciding). What do you think now that we have discussed everything? Which do you want to do?" Write response in "Choice" space on page 5 of the Record Form.

2.   *Probe.* Consider whether the final choice follows logically from the patient's previous reasoning and generated consequences. If so, no probe is needed. If it

does not, discuss the inconsistencies with the patient and describe the process in the "Logical Consistency of Choice" space on page 5 of the Record Form.

III. RATING

Responses on the MacCAT-T Record Form provide the content for rating patients' responses. Guidelines for the rating process are provided below, as well as ways to combine the ratings to arrive at average ratings for various parts of the MacCAT-T (Understanding, Appreciation, Reasoning). Record summary ratings on page 6 of the MacCAT-T Record Form.

UNDERSTANDING

Rating the Items

The following guidelines are used to score each item in the three Understanding sections of the MacCAT-T procedure (the Disorder, Treatment, and Benefits/Risks sections).

2 Rating

Patient recalls the content of the item and offers a fairly clear version of it. A verbatim repetition of the clinician's description is not required; in fact, paraphrase in the patient's own words is preferred.

For Benefit/Risk items, the patient must provide a reasonably accurate indication of the likelihood that the benefit/risk will be experienced, if this was described in the disclosure.

1 Rating

Patient shows some recollection of the item content, but describes it in a way that renders understanding uncertain, even after the clinician has made efforts to obtain clarification from the patient.

Examples include responses that could possibly indicate understanding but are too broad or vague to be sure (e.g., for pain of surgery, "It might make me feel uncomfortable"), or responses that contain some specific and correct piece of information but lack some other part of the critical content (e.g., for hallucinations, "I might hear things").

0 Rating

Patient (a) does not recall the content of the item; (b) describes it in a way that is clearly inaccurate; or (c) describes it in a way that seriously distorts its meaning, even after the clinician has made efforts to obtain clarification from the patient.

Constructing Understanding Summary Ratings

For each of the three Understanding sections (Disorder, Treatment, Benefits/Risks):

- Add the ratings for all items in the section.
- Divide that sum by the number of items to find the *Subscale Rating*. This produces Subscale Ratings between 2.0 and 0.0 for Understanding-Disorder, Understanding-Treatment, and Understanding-Benefits/Risks.

When the Subscale Ratings for each of the three Understanding sections have been obtained, add them to produce an overall *Understanding Summary Rating*. This produces an Understanding Rating between 6.0 and 0.0.

APPRECIATION

Rating the Items

Somewhat different rating guidelines are necessary for the Appreciation-Disorder and Appreciation-Treatment items.

> ### Appreciation-Disorder

2 Rating

Patient acknowledges that he or she manifests the disclosed disorder, and all or most of the disclosed symptoms.

OR

Patient does *not* agree with the preceding, but offers reasons that are not delusional and have some reasonable explanation. Some examples of "reasonable" explanations:

- "Another doctor just told me something else."
- "I had all these symptoms last year, and at that time the doctors gave me a different diagnosis."
- "In my culture (referring accurately to the patient's cultural background), this is not considered unusual or a 'sickness'."

1 Rating

Patient acknowledges manifesting the disorder and some of the disclosed symptoms but does not acknowledge other symptoms that are critical to understanding the disorder and/or its treatment.

OR

Patient disagrees or is ambivalent about the existence of the disorder or the symptoms, but for reasons that are vague or not clearly expressed.

0 Rating

Patient clearly does not agree that he or she has the disclosed disorder, with reasoning based on a delusional premise or some other belief that seriously distorts reality and does not have a reasonable basis in the patient's cultural or religious background.

OR

Patient believes that the symptoms are related to circumstances other than a medical/psychiatric disorder (e.g., psychotic symptoms seen simply as consequences of work-related stress; viral disease as "merely fatigue - working too hard").

OR

Patient clearly disagrees with symptoms or disorder, but with no comprehensible explanation offered.

Appreciation-Treatment

2 Rating

Patient acknowledges at least some potential for the treatment to produce some benefit, and the reason given is not based on a delusional premise or a serious distortion of reality.

OR

Patient does *not* believe that the treatment has the potential to produce some benefit, but offers reasons that are not delusional and have some reasonable explanation. Examples of "reasonable" explanations:

- Explanations that are consistent with the patient's religious beliefs (or cultural background) that medical treatment generally is not of real value.
- Explanations based on past experience with the treatment in question (e.g., having taken psychoactive medication often in the past with little or no benefit, or knowing others who have made this claim).

1 Rating

Patient does or does not believe that the treatment has the potential to produce some benefit but the reason is vague or does not allow the examiner to determine whether the reason represents delusional thinking or serious distortion of reality.

OR

Patient is ambivalent concerning whether the treatment has potential to produce some benefit.

0 Rating

Patient acknowledges at least some potential for the treatment to produce some benefit, but for reasons that appear to be based on a delusional premise or a serious distortion of reality.

OR

Patient does *not* believe that the treatment has the potential to produce any benefit, and offers reasons that appear to be delusional or a serious distortion of reality.

NOTE: Failures to acknowledge the potential benefit of treatment may obtain a 0 rating not only if they are based on delusional belief systems, but also if they are strongly influenced by extremes in affective symptoms (e.g., mania, severe depression).

Appreciation Summary Ratings

Add the ratings from the two Appreciation sections to obtain an *Appreciation Summary Rating*, which will be between 4.0 and 0.0.

REASONING

Rating the Items

The following guidelines are used to rate the four Reasoning items (Consequential Reasoning, Comparative Reasoning, Generating Consequences, and Logical Consistency).

Consequential Reasoning

2 Rating

Patient mentions at least two specific consequences when explaining the choice. The consequences may be related to only one or to more than one treatment option. The consequences need not be for treatments or alternatives that were in the disclosure. The consequences must be more specific than "_____ will help me" or "_____ will make me feel better." For example:

- "With medication, the voices I hear will go away."
- "I would be able to walk with less pain."

1 Rating

Patient mentions only one specific consequence when explaining the choice.

0 Rating

Patient mentions no specific consequences when explaining the choice, even after being asked whether there were any "more specific reasons why that choice seems best."

Comparative Reasoning

2 Rating

Patient offers at least one statement in the form of a comparison of at least two options, with the comparison including a statement of at least one specific difference. For example: "With treatment X, I am more likely to be able to walk places than with treatment Y." "Treatment X will work faster." (Note that the comparative clause "than with treatment Y" can be inferred from the word "faster.")

NOTE: A comparison can be assumed when the patient's reason for choosing one treatment is the *absence* of some negative consequence of another treatment option that is not being stated. For example:

- "The surgery seems best, because then I won't have to be in the hospital a long time."
- "I prefer the medication X, so that I won't have to be so drowsy" (a side-effect of an alternative medication).

1 Rating

Patient makes comparison statement, but does not include a statement of a specific consequence. For example, "Treatment X is better than treatment Y," without being able to say specifically how X is better.

0 Rating

Patient makes no comparative statements.

Generating Consequences

2 Rating

Patient gives at least two reasonable everyday consequences, including at least one for each of the two inquiry questions. For example:

- "With treatment X, I'll still be able to walk to places I go in my neighborhood."

- "With medication Y, it sounds like I might be drowsy a lot - could be dangerous at work."

NOTE: Everyday consequences must go beyond the consequences that were in the disclosure, and must refer to practical everyday activities or social relationships. For example, if drowsiness is a side-effect of a medication, "I would be sleepy" is not sufficient; "I might have trouble awaking and be late for work all the time" is sufficient.

1 Rating

Patient gives one or more reasonable everyday consequences for one of the inquiry questions, but none for the other.

0 Rating

Patient gives no reasonable everyday consequences, even with adequate encouragement.

Logical Consistency

2 Rating

Patient's final choice follows logically from the patient's own reasoning, as put forth by patient's responses when explaining the choice.

1 Rating

It is not clear whether the final choice follows logically from the patient's reasoning when explaining the choice.

0 Rating

Patient's final choice clearly does not follow logically from patient's previous reasoning.

Reasoning Summary Ratings

Add the ratings from the four Reasoning sections to obtain a *Reasoning Summary Rating,* which will be between 8.0 and 0.0.

EXPRESSING A CHOICE

Rating the Item

The following guidelines are used to rate the one item for Expressing a Choice.

2 Rating

Patient states a choice, or patient indicates desire for professional or other responsible person (e.g., relatives) to make the choice.

1 Rating

Patient states two or three choices, seems ambivalent.

0 Rating

Patient states no choice.

IV. Interpretation

As noted earlier in this manual, the MacCAT-T should be used in the context of a broader range of clinical information, described in *Assessing Competence to Consent to Treatment* (Grisso & Appelbaum, 1998). That book also describes in detail the process of making interpretations, and the limits of interpretations, about competence based on data from the MacCAT-T.

It is important to recognize that *the MacCAT-T does not provide scores that translate directly into determinations of legal competence or incompetence.* Patients with MacCAT-T Summary Ratings that are in the "average" or better range on the norms for all four types of MacCAT-T abilities are very likely to have sufficient decisional abilities to support a judgment of competence to make most types of treatment decisions. In contrast, while very low MacCAT-T Summary Ratings suggest the possibility of incompetence to make treatment decisions, low ratings alone rarely will provide an adequate basis for making the final judgment. Considered alone, the MacCAT-T Summary Ratings should be interpreted as indicating no more than the level of performance of the patient on the MacCAT-T interview. Those ratings themselves must then be interpreted clinically in order to describe the meaning of the patient's MacCAT-T performance. This will require the use of clinical observations derived from diagnostic assessment, mental status examination, and psychiatric or psychosocial history, as well as consideration of the decisionmaking task(s) with which the patient is confronted.

MacCAT-T scores, therefore, are useful when combined with a clinical process for determining *why* the patient manifested deficits in the decisionmaking abilities assessed with the MacCAT-T: for example, whether the patient's performance represents the best that the patient currently can do, and how or whether the patient's apparent deficits in decisionmaking abilities on the MacCAT-T are related to (caused by) the patient's mental disorder. In addition, clinical interpretation is necessary in order to address the degree to which - and how - the deficits in MacCAT-T performance and abilities might be remediable.

23

During 1994, the authors conducted a modest study of the MacCAT-T's performance with a group of patients in Worcester State Hospital with schizophrenia or schizoaffective disorder, as well as a matched "normal" comparison group of subjects in the Worcester community who did not meet criteria for schizophrenia (Grisso & Appelbaum, 1997). Data from that study, as well as information on inter-rater reliability, are provided in Tables 1-7 (pp. 29-35). In some clinical cases, these may be useful to clinicians as a baseline for comparing their own patients' performances.

REFERENCES

Appelbaum, P. S., & Grisso, T. (1988). Assessing patients' capacities to consent to treatment. *New England Journal of Medicine, 319,* 1635-1638.

Appelbaum, P. S., & Grisso, T. (1995). The MacArthur Treatment Competence Study, I: Mental illness and competence to consent to treatment. *Law and Human Behavior, 19,* 105-126.

Appelbaum, P. S., & Roth, L. (1981). Clinical issues in the assessment of competency. *American Journal of Psychiatry, 138,* 1462-1467.

Appelbaum, P. S., & Roth, L. (1982). Competence to consent to research: A psychiatric overview. *Archives of General Psychiatry, 39,* 951-958.

Berg, J., Appelbaum, P. S., & Grisso, T. (1996). Constructing competence: Formulating standards of legal competence to make medical decisions. *Rutgers Law Review, 48,* 345-396.

Grisso, T., & Appelbaum, P. S. (1995). The MacArthur Treatment Competence Study, III: Abilities of patients to consent to psychiatric and medical treatment. *Law and Human Behavior, 19,* 149-174.

Grisso, T., & Appelbaum, P. S. (1997). The MacCAT-T: A clinical tool to assess patients' capacities to make treatment decisions. *Psychiatric Services, 48,* 1415-1419.

Grisso, T., & Appelbaum, P. S. (1998). *Assessing Competence to Consent to Treatment: A Guide for Physicians and Other Health Professionals.* New York: Oxford University Press.

Grisso, T., Appelbaum, P. S., Mulvey, E., & Fletcher, K. (1995). The MacArthur Treatment Competence Study, II: Measures of abilities related to competence to consent to treatment. *Law and Human Behavior, 19,* 127-148.

TABLES

Variables	Patients Hospitalized With Schizophrenia $n = 40$	Community (non-ill) $n = 40$
TABLE 1 Sample Description for MacCAT-T Study		
Age (Mean)	39.1	39.0
(Standard Deviation)	9.6	9.9
Male (%)	80	80
White (%)	85	85
Socioeconomic Level (IV-V) (%)	87	80
Schizophrenia or Schizoaffective Disorder (%)	100	0
Involuntary Commitment (%)	23	NA
Days from Admission to Testing (Mean)	4.2	NA
Number of Prior Admissions, Three or More (%)	85	NA
Brief Psychiatric Rating Scale Total (Mean)	50.2	NA
(Standard Deviation)	(8.5)	

TABLE 2
Frequencies and Percentages for
Understanding Scores

	Hospital		Community	
	n	%	*n*	%
Understanding 1 (Disorder)				
2.00-1.70	18	45.0	32	80.0
1.69-1.30	9	22.5	6	15.0
1.29-1.00	7	17.5	2	5.0
< 1.00	6	15.0	0	0.0
Mean	1.46		1.83	
Standard Deviation	.60		.23	
Understanding 2 (Treatment)				
2.00-1.70	26	65.0	37	92.5
1.69-1.30	9	22.5	2	5.0
1.29-1.00	1	2.5	0	0.0
< 1.00	4	10.0	1	2.5
Mean	1.66		1.94	
Standard Deviation	.55		.24	
Understanding 3 (Benefits/Risks)				
2.00-1.70	10	25.0	31	77.5
1.69-1.30	7	17.5	5	12.5
1.29-1.00	13	32.5	3	7.5
< 1.00	10	25.0	1	2.5
Mean	1.20		1.83	
Standard Deviation	.56		.34	
Understanding Total				
6.0-5.1	13	32.5	36	90.0
5.0-4.1	14	35.0	2	5.0
4.0-3.1	6	15.0	2	5.0
3.0-2.1	5	12.5	0	0.0
< 2.1	2	5.0	0	0.0
Mean	4.33		5.60	
Standard Deviation	1.35		.66	

$t = 5.19 \quad p = .000$

TABLE 3
Frequencies and Percentages for
Appreciation Scores

	Hospital	
	n	*%*
Appreciation 1 (Disorder)		
Full Credit (2)	31	77.5
Partial Credit (1)	4	10.0
No Credit (0)	5	12.5
Appreciation 2 (Treatment)		
Full Credit (2)	36	90.0
Partial Credit (1)	1	2.5
No Credit (0)	3	7.5
Appreciation Total		
Full Credit (4)	31	77.5
(3)	2	5.0
Partial Credit (2)	3	7.5
(1)	3	7.5
No Credit (0)	1	2.5

TABLE 4
Frequencies and Percentages for
Reasoning Scores

Variables	Hospital		Community	
	n	*%*	*n*	*%*
Consequential Thinking				
Full Credit (2)	18	45.0	28	70.0
Partial Credit (1)	15	37.5	7	17.5
No Credit (0)	7	17.5	5	12.5
Mean	1.28		1.58	
Standard Deviation	.75		.71	
Comparative Thinking				
Full Credit (2)	16	40.0	17	42.5
Partial Credit (1)	4	10.0	4	10.0
No Credit (0)	20	50.0	19	47.5
Mean	.90		.95	
Standard Deviation	.96		.96	
Generating Consequences				
Full Credit (2)	24	60.0	34	85.0
Partial Credit (1)	8	20.0	3	7.5
No Credit (0)	8	20.0	3	7.5
Mean	1.40		1.78	
Standard Deviation	.81		.57	
Logical Reasoning				
Full Credit (2)	31	77.5	35	87.5
Partial Credit (1)	3	7.5	4	10.0
No Credit (0)	6	15.0	1	2.5
Mean	1.63		1.85	
Standard Deviation	.74		.42	
Reasoning Total				
8.0	8	20.0	12	30.0
7.0-6.0	13	32.5	16	40.0
5.0-4.0	11	27.5	10	25.0
3.0-2.0	2	5.0	1	2.5
1.0-0.0	6	15.0	1	2.5
Mean	5.20		6.15	
Standard Deviation	2.42		1.69	

$t = 2.15$ $p = .038$

TABLE 5
Frequencies and Percentages for
Expressing a Choice

	Hospital		Community	
	n	*%*	*n*	*%*
Full Credit (2)	38	95.0	40	100.0
Partial Credit (1)	1	2.5	0	0.0
No Credit (0)	1	2.5	0	0.0

$t = 1.36$ $p = .183$

TABLE 6
Intraclass Correlations (ICC) Among Three Raters,
and Pearson _r_ Correlations Between Pairs of Raters
(_n_ = 40: 20 Patients and 20 Community
Comparisons), for Summary Scores

	All Raters (ICC)	Raters		
		1-2	1-3	2-3
Understanding Total	.99	.97	.99	.97
Appreciation Total	.87	.72	.59	.81
Reasoning Total	.91	.83	.77	.75

NOTE: Correlations for Appreciation Total is based on ratings of 20 patients.

TABLE 7
Intraclass Correlations (ICC) Among Three Raters, and Pearson *r* Correlations Between Pairs of Raters (*n* = 40: 20 Patients and 20 Community Comparisons), For Sections of the MacCAT-T

	All Raters (ICC)	Raters		
		1-2	1-3	2-3
Understanding: Disorder	.98	.95	.98	.96
Understanding: Treatment	.98	.97	.95	.96
Understanding: Benefits/Risks	.99	.97	.98	.97
Appreciation: Disorder	.91	.86	.70	.80
Appreciation: Treatment	.85	.66	.69	.74
Reasoning: Consequential Thinking	.82	.69	.58	.51
Reasoning: Comparative Thinking	.88	.82	.70	.64
Reasoning: Generating Consequences	.92	.80	.81	.77
Reasoning: Logical Consistency	.88	.77	.73	.66
Expressing a Choice	.97	.89	.89	1.00

NOTE: Correlations for "Appreciation: Disorder" and "Appreciation: Treatment" are based on ratings of 20 patients.

MacCAT-T Record
Form and
Alternative
Treatment (AT) Form

MacCAT-T RECORD FORM

Patient: _____ **Clinician:** _____

Date: _____ **Time:** _____ **Unit:** _____

UNDERSTANDING-DISORDER

Disclose: "Now please explain in your own words what I've said about your condition."
Probe (if necessary): Re-Disclose and Re-Inquire (if necessary).

Disclosure	Patient Response
#1 Diagnosis	Rating ☐
#2 Feature of Disorder	Rating ☐
#3 Feature of Disorder	Rating ☐
#4 Feature of Disorder	Rating ☐
#5 Course of Disorder	Rating ☐
	Understanding-Disorder (Sum) ☐
Other	

MacArthur Competence Assessment Tool for Treatment (MacCAT-T)
Copyright © 1998 Professional Resource Exchange, Inc.
Thomas Grisso and Paul S. Appelbaum / University of Massachusetts Medical School
Developed with support from the John D. and Catherine T. MacArthur Foundation

APPRECIATION-DISORDER

Inquire: "Now that is what we think is the problem in your case. If you have any reason to doubt that, I'd like you to tell me so. What do you think?"

☐ Agrees   ☐ Disagrees   ☐ Ambivalent

Probe: If patient disagrees or is ambivalent, description of disagreement and patient's explanation.

Explanation	
	Appreciation-Disorder ☐

UNDERSTANDING-TREATMENT

Disclose: "Now please explain in your own words what I've said about this treatment."
Probe (if necessary): Re-Disclose and Re-Inquire (if necessary).

Disclosure	**Patient Response**
#1 Name of Treatment	
	Rating ☐
#2 Feature of Treatment	
	Rating ☐
#3 Feature of Treatment	
	Rating ☐
#4 Feature of Treatment	
	Rating ☐
	Understanding-Treatment (Sum) ☐
Other	

UNDERSTANDING-BENEFITS/RISKS

Disclose: "Now please explain in your own words what I've said about benefits and risks of this treatment."

Probe (if necessary):   Re-Disclose and Re-Inquire (if necessary).

Disclosure	Patient Response
#1 Benefit	Rating ☐
#2 Benefit	Rating ☐
#3 Risk	Rating ☐
#4 Risk	Rating ☐

Understanding-Benefits/Risks (Sum) ☐

Other	

APPRECIATION-TREATMENT

Inquire: "You might or might not decide that this is the treatment you want - we'll talk about it later. But do you think it's possible that this treatment might be of some benefit to you?"

☐ Agrees   ☐ Disagrees   ☐ Ambivalent

Probe: "So you feel that it is/isn't possible for that treatment to be of some help for your condition. Can you explain that to me? What makes it seem that the treatment would/wouldn't be of possible benefit to you?"

	Appreciation-Treatment

ALTERNATIVE TREATMENTS

See Alternative Treatment (AT) Forms, one for each Alternative Treatment.

FIRST CHOICE AND REASONING

Choice: "Now let's review the choices that you have. First . . .; second . . .; and so on (name each treatment option reviewed earlier, including no-treatment option). Which of these seems best for you? Which do you think you are most likely to want?"

Choice _____

Inquire: "You think that (state patient's choice) might be best. Tell me what it is that makes that seem better than the others."

Probe: Discuss explanation to explore reasoning process.

Explanation	
	Consequential
	Comparative

GENERATE CONSEQUENCES

Inquire-1: "I told you about some of the possible benefits and risks or discomforts of (name the patient's preferred treatment option). What are some ways that these might influence your everyday activities at home or at work?"

Consequences-1
Consequences-1 [ ]

Inquire-2: "Now let's consider (name of any other treatment or the no-treatment option). What are some ways that the outcomes of that option might influence your everyday activities at home or at work?"

Consequences-2
Consequences-2 [ ]

Generate Consequences (Sum) [ ]

FINAL CHOICE

Inquire: "When we started this discussion you favored (insert 'First Choice' from earlier inquiry, or note that the patient seemed to be having difficulty deciding). What do you think now that we have discussed everything? Which do you want to do?"

Choice
Express Choice [ ]

LOGICAL CONSISTENCY OF CHOICE

Examiner's Explanation
Logical Consistency [ ]

MacCAT-T RATING SUMMARY

	Sum of Ratings	÷	Number of Items		Subtotal Rating
UNDERSTANDING					
Disorder	_____	÷	_____	=	_____
Treatment	_____	÷	_____	=	_____
Benefits/Risks	_____	÷	_____	=	_____

Understanding Summary Rating (0-6) ☐

APPRECIATION

Disorder _____

Treatment _____

Appreciation Summary Rating (0-4) ☐

REASONING

Consequential _____

Comparative _____

Generate Consequences _____

Logical Consistency _____

Reasoning Summary Rating (0-8) ☐

Expressing A Choice Summary Rating (0-2) ☐

OPTIONAL: Summary scores for Understanding of each alternative treatment

Alternative 1:   Alternative 3:

Alternative 2:   Alternative 4:

ALTERNATIVE TREATMENT (AT) FORM

To Record Understanding for an Alternative Treatment
(Side 1: Treatment) (Side 2: Benefits/Risks)

Patient: _____

UNDERSTANDING-TREATMENT

Disclose: "Now please explain in your own words what I said about this treatment."
Probe (if necessary): Re-Disclose and Re-Inquire (if necessary).

Disclosure	**Patient Response**
#1 Name of Treatment	Rating ☐
#2 Feature of Treatment	Rating ☐
#3 Feature of Treatment	Rating ☐
#4 Feature of Treatment	Rating ☐

Understanding-Treatment (Sum) ☐

Other	

(over)

UNDERSTANDING-BENEFITS/RISKS

Disclose: "Now please explain in your own words what I've said about benefits and risks of this treatment."

Probe (if necessary): Re-Disclose and Re-Inquire (if necessary).

Disclosure	Patient Response
#1 Benefit	Rating ☐
#2 Benefit	Rating ☐
#3 Risk	Rating ☐
#4 Risk	Rating ☐

Understanding-Benefits/Risks (Sum) ☐

Disclosure	Patient Response
Other	